THE FOUR HORSEMEN OF THE APOCALYPSE, 1921

UNCHARTED SEAS, 1921

CAMILLE, 1921

CAMILLE, 1921
(Nazimova)

THE SHEIK, 1921

THE SHEIK, 1921
(Agnes Ayres)

BEYOND THE ROCKS, 1922   BEYOND THE ROCKS, 1922

BEYOND THE ROCKS, 1922

BEYOND THE ROCKS, 1922
(Gloria Swanson)

BLOOD AND SAND, 1922

BLOOD AND SAND, 1922

BLOOD AND SAND, 1922
*(jacket and cape
for bullfighter's costume)*

BLOOD AND SAND, 1922

BLOOD AND SAND, 1922
(Nita Naldi)

THE YOUNG RAJAH, 1922

THE YOUNG RAJAH, 1922
(Wanda Hawley)

THE YOUNG RAJAH, 1922

Party costume; dressed as Nijinsky in ''L'Après-Midi d'un Faune.'' (The only fabric is the leather pouch; the rest is body paint.)

MONSIEUR BEAUCAIRE, 1924

MONSIEUR BEAUCAIRE, 1924

MONSIEUR BEAUCAIRE, 1924
(Bebe Daniels)

Valentino and his wife, Natacha Rambova, on a dance tour for Mineralava, a face cream

THE EAGLE, 1925

THE EAGLE, 1925
(Louise Dresser)

14

A test for a never-produced film   COBRA, 1925